To

From

Daughters are more precious
than gold.
More precious than any
inanimate thing, however beautiful.
More precious than anyone's
dreams, however glorious.
More precious than one's life.
For they light the way
into the future.
They are your gift to the world.
They are its hope.
And yours to love.

More than
we ever
dreamed...

Dearest Daughter –
we were wonder-struck when
we first saw your face,
first held your tiny hands.
We did not know that moment
was only the beginning of wonders.
You have become more
than even we ever dreamed.

Stronger than

Like it or not, we are bound to one another. It is the lightest of links – so light that sometimes we seem to forget it altogether. But it is stronger than life itself. One tiny tug will have me dropping anything I'm doing – you are, above everything, the heartbeat of my life.

ife...

The best...

Looking about me
at all the shapes, sizes
and creeds, careers and
cleverness that daughters
come in – I am amazed.
– And the very best one of all,
of course, is you.

I'm proud of you
not for the things
that came easily to you –
or that were part of you from
the very beginning –
but for your slogging it out
against the odds and
against your nature
and spluttering to the surface
with your prize.

Do you remember
walking by a shining sea
and the sound of gulls?
Lopsided birthday cakes?
Walks through spring woods?
I do, I do.

I wish you the beauty of silence, the glory of sunlight, the mystery of darkness, the force of flame, the power of water, the sweetness of air, the quiet strength of earth, the love that lies at the very root of things. I wish you the wonder of living.

Do you remember
when I told you that everything
comes in useful
in the end? All the mistakes,
all the pain, all the loss –
just as much as the hard work
and the learning and the love.
We've proved it true.
We'll go on proving it.

You called today
and the sun came out.

However sad I am
a note, a phone call, a text
from you
brings me happiness.

I share your joys and successes
– but never forget
I'm here for you
when things go wrong.

Daughters...

I have to let go your hands.
But the joys we knew before,
remembered or lost,
are part of us forever.

A mother loves her children
as they are now – the sum
of all the ages she has known
and loved. She's saved
the shadows of those days –
the drawings, the gifts, the letters
– and treasures them.
But she loves best what is here
and now – and awaits the future
with a happy heart.

I keep all the photographs
of you – as if I could hold on
to all the different yous –
the baby, the toddler,
the schoolgirl,
the teenager.
But they don't really matter.
Not that much.
Because you are all of them –
and every time
I see you I think
"This is the best time."

I wish you discoveries
and marvels.
I wish you success.
I wish you joy and peace
and deep contentment.
And always, always love.

I am so very ordinary.
How then did I produce
a girl like you?
So beautiful, so clever
and so kind.